WONDER
FROM (

BY
MARGERY GREEN

MACMILLAN

First published 1961 by
MACMILLAN EDUCATION LTD
London and Oxford
Companies and representatives throughout the world

www.macmillan-africa.com

ISBN 0–333–05711–2

42	41	40	39	38	37	36	35	34	33
09	08	07	06	05	04	03	02	01	00

This book is printed on paper suitable for recycling and made from fully managed and sustained forest sources.

Printed in Malaysia

MACMILLAN STORIES TO REMEMBER SERIES
JUNIOR TITLES

Black Beauty *by Anna Sewell*
Call of the Wild *by Jack London*
Captain Blood *by Rafael Sabatini*
Frankenstein *by Mary Shelley*
Gulliver's Travels *by Jonathan Swift*
Ivanhoe *by Sir Walter Scott*
Just-So Stories *by Rudyard Kipling*
Kim *by Rudyard Kipling*
Little Women *by Louisa May Alcott*
Lorna Doone *by R.D. Blackmore*
Lost Horizon *by James Hilton*
Moby Dick *by Herman Melville*
Moonfleet *by John Meade Falkner*
National Velvet *by Enid Bagnold*
Nicholas Nickleby *by Charles Dickens*
Oliver Twist *by Charles Dickens*
Robinson Crusoe *by Daniel Defoe*
Round the World in Eighty Days *by Jules Verne*
Silas Marner *by George Eliot*
Six Short Stories
Six Tales from Shakespeare
Stories from Homer
Stange Tales from the Arabian Nights
The Adventures of Huckleberry Finn *by Mark Twain*
The Mayor of Casterbridge *by Thomas Hardy*
The Turn of the Screw *by Henry James*
The Vicar of Wakefield *by Oliver Goldsmith*
Tom Brown's Schooldays *by Thomas Hughes*
Tom Sawyer *by Mark Twain*
Treasure Island *by R.L. Stevenson*
Wonder Tales from Greece

MODERN STORIES TO REMEMBER

All Quiet on the Western Front *by Erich Maria Remarque*
A Passage to India *by E.M. Forster*
Cakes and Ale *by Somerset Maugham*
Goodbye, Mr Chips *by James Hilton*
On the Beach *by Nevil Shute*
The Black Cloud *by Fred Hoyle*
The Great Gatsby *by F. Scott Fitzgerald*
The Gun *by C.S. Forester*
The Rocking Horse Winner, The White Stocking
   and Strike-Pay *by D.H. Lawrence*

MACMILLAN STORIES TO REMEMBER SERIES
SENIOR TITLES

PREFACE

This book has been specially adapted for those for whom English is a second or foreign language, and who have reached at least a lower intermediate level. It will be suitable, in fact, for anyone who finds the original book too long or too difficult.

Difficult sentence structures have been avoided, though every effort has been made to retain something of the style of the original.

CONTENTS

1. THE GORGON'S HEAD

WHEN Perseus was a very little boy, he and his mother were put into a wooden chest and floated out to sea. Danaë was the name of his mother, and she was the daughter of a king. There were wicked men in her country who hoped to get rid of Danaë and her child in this way.

The mother held her son closely in her arms as the wooden chest floated far out from the land. The waves tossed them up and down but the chest did not sink. It came at last one evening to the shore of an island, where it was caught in a fisherman's net and safely brought to land. The wooden chest on its strange voyage had come by chance to the island of Seriphus.

Fortune had favoured the mother and child, for the fisherman was a good and kind man. He took Danaë and Perseus to live with him and he looked after them with great kindness. As the years went by, Perseus grew big and handsome and strong; and he became skilful with his sword and shield, as was the custom in those days.

Now the fisherman had a brother who was ruler of the island of Seriphus, and his name was Polydectes. He was not good and kind like his brother the fisherman; he was wicked and cruel.

7

When this wicked king saw that Perseus was now a young man, he decided to send him on some dangerous errand. He might perhaps be killed and then Danaë would be left alone without her son, and this would please the wicked king. At last King Polydectes sent for Perseus.

The young man came to the palace and stood before the king's throne.

'Perseus,' said the king, 'you and your mother have received much kindness from my brother and me. I expect you would be glad to repay us in some way.'

'I would willingly risk my life to do so, your Majesty,' answered Perseus.

'Then I have a little adventure for you,' said the king. 'As you are brave and daring, it will give you a chance to show your strength. You have heard that I am soon to marry the beautiful Princess Hippodamia? It is usual to give the bride a present that is rare and interesting. Today I have thought of just the thing.'

'And can I help you to obtain it?' asked Perseus, eagerly.

'You can, if you are brave enough,' said King Polydectes. 'I wish to give the princess the head of the Gorgon Medusa. Bring that to me and I shall be very pleased with you.'

'I will set off tomorrow morning,' answered the young man.

'And Perseus,' added the king, ' be careful not to damage the head when you cut it off. I want it in very good condition when I give it to Princess Hippodamia.'

As soon as Perseus had left the palace the king laughed cruelly, for he knew that he had asked the young man to do something which was almost impossible.

The people of the island soon heard the news that Perseus had undertaken to cut off the head of Medusa and they rejoiced. They were nearly all as wicked as the king himself and they hoped for some misfortune to come to Danaë and her son. The only good man on the island seems to have been the fisherman who helped them.

Now, at that time there were three Gorgons. They were the most strange and terrible monsters that had ever been seen since the world began, and Medusa was one of them. They were three sisters, but anything less like women can hardly be imagined. They were more like a kind of dragon and their bodies were covered with armour of iron. Instead of hair, each of them had a hundred snakes growing on their heads, alive and twisting and turning, each with its poisonous tongue that darted in and out of its mouth. The Gorgons had teeth like tigers' tusks, and their claw-like hands were made of brass. They had huge wings that shone bright and dazzling in the sun, for every feather was made of gold.

If anyone happened to see a Gorgon flying in the sunshine, he ran to hide as quickly as he could. It was not only the snakes on the Gorgons' heads that made people afraid, nor the thought of those terrible teeth and claws—though they were bad enough. No, the worst danger from these dreadful creatures was that if anyone looked them in the face he was immediately turned to stone!

And so Perseus had a difficult task indeed. He had to fight a terrible monster and cut off its head; he had to kill a Gorgon with golden wings, iron body, tiger teeth, brazen[1] claws, snaky hair—but he must not look at the awful monster, or he would be turned into stone.

Perseus did not tell his mother about the difficult task that the king had given him. He put on his sword and he took his shield, and then he rowed a boat over to the mainland. Here he sat down in a quiet place and thought about what he had to do. The difficulty and danger of his task made him very thoughtful indeed.

While he sat there, a voice suddenly spoke beside him.

' Perseus, why are you sad?'

He lifted his head and found that he was not alone. A man stood beside him; a bright, intelligent-looking young man in a cloak. He had a strange cap on his head, a twisted staff in his hand,

---

1. *brazen:* made of brass

and a crooked sword hanging by his side. He looked so gay and lively, and he seemed so ready to be cheerful and helpful that Perseus felt better at once.

' I am thinking about a difficult adventure that I have undertaken,' he said.

' Well, I have helped many a young man, in difficulties that looked very alarming at first,' said the stranger. ' You may have heard of me. Sometimes I am called Mercury, but Quicksilver suits me just as well. Let us talk the matter over and perhaps I may be able to help you.'

At once Perseus felt he could trust this young man with all his story. He told how King Polydectes wanted the head of the Gorgon Medusa, and how he had undertaken to get it for him, but he was afraid of being turned into stone.

' And that would be a great pity,' said Quicksilver, with a smile. ' I'm sure you would rather be a young man for a few more years than a stone statue for a very long time—even if it was a handsome one!' He then went on to tell Perseus that the first thing to do was to find the Three Grey Women.

' The Three Grey Women!' cried Perseus. ' I have never heard of them.'

' They are three very strange old women,' said Quicksilver. ' They have only one eye between them and only one tooth. We must find them by starlight or in the twilight[2] of the evening, for they never show themselves in the light of the sun or the moon.'

' But why should I waste time in looking for these Grey Women,' asked Perseus, ' when it is the Gorgons that I have to find?'

' There are other things to be done before you come to them,' said his new friend. ' Now, first you must polish your shield until you can see your face in it clearly.'

Perseus thought it was more important that his shield was strong, but he set to work with a will. He polished as hard as he could, until his shield shone like the moon at harvest time. He nodded and smiled at his bright reflection in the shield. Quicksilver did the same; then he took off his own short and crooked sword and put it on Perseus, instead of the one he was wearing.

' This sword can cut easily through iron and brass,' Quicksilver said. ' Now we must be going.'

He set off very fast and Perseus found it hard to keep up. He looked sideways at Quicksilver several times as they went along. He fancied that he saw wings on his feet and at the sides of his head, but when he looked again he found he was mistaken.

Quicksilver soon saw that Perseus was out of breath. ' Here,' he said, ' you take the staff, for you need it more than I do.'

2. *twilight:* half light.

12

'Here,' he said, 'you take the staff.'

'I could go faster,' Perseus said, looking again at his companion's feet, 'if only I had a pair of winged shoes!'

'We must see if we can get you a pair,' answered Quicksilver, as they set off again.

Perseus found himself going much faster now. The stick seemed to be alive in his hand and it lent him new life.

When at last they found the Three Grey Women, Perseus was astonished to see that they used their one eye in turn. It was only by cleverly capturing this eye, and leaving the Three Grey Women in darkness for a while, that Perseus and his friend made them tell how best the Three Nymphs could be found.

These Nymphs had in their charge three things which Perseus must have to succeed in his adventure: the magic wallet, the flying slippers and the helmet of invisibility.

The Three Nymphs were very different from the Three Grey Women. They were young and beautiful instead of being old, and they each had two bright eyes of their own instead of only one between them. They seemed to know Quicksilver well, and when he told them about Perseus and his adventure they at once offered to help.

First they brought to Perseus the magic wallet. It was like a purse made of deer-skin, and it was beautifully embroidered.[3] Then they brought a pair of slippers, with a nice little pair of wings at the heel of each.

' Put them on, Perseus,' Quicksilver said.

Perseus knelt down and began to put one on, while he placed the other beside him on the ground. Suddenly, this other slipper spread its wings and began to fly upwards. It was only Quicksilver's leap in the air that luckily caught it in time.

' You must be more careful,' he said to Perseus. ' It would frighten the birds in the sky if they saw a flying slipper!'

---

3. *embroidered:* decorated with needle-work

When both the slippers were safely on his feet, Perseus found it quite difficult to stay on the ground. The slippers began to take him up into the air at once.

' It is always difficult to manage these high-flying affairs at first,' said Quicksilver, laughing at him, ' but you must wait for the invisible helmet.' The Nymphs had it all ready for him to put on. And then there happened something that was more wonderful than anything Perseus had known before. One moment he stood there, brave and handsome, with the crooked sword at his side and the brightly polished shield on his arm—and the next moment, he had disappeared!

' Where are you?' asked Quicksilver.

As soon as the helmet was on, Perseus was invisible —even the helmet itself could not be seen!

' Why, here, of course—just where I was a moment ago,' answered Perseus. 'Can't you see me?'

' No,' said his friend, ' and the Gorgons won't see you, either. Quick—follow me, and let us try your skill with the winged slippers.'

As Quicksilver said this, the cap on his head spread its wings too, and off they flew, hundreds of feet up into the air.

By now the moon was shining bright, and Perseus thought he would like nothing better than to fly towards it, up and up, and spend the rest of his life there. Then he looked down and saw the earth

15

below him in the light of the moon. He could see its lakes and its rivers shining like silver, its snowy mountains, its green fields and woods, its cities of white marble; and he knew it was as beautiful as any moon or star could be. Besides all this, he saw the island of Seriphus where his dear mother was.

Perseus noticed that the clouds looked like silver castles in the distance, but when he came to them he found himself cold and damp with mist, until he flew out of them again into the moonlight.

As they flew along, Perseus fancied he could hear the sound of other wings beside him.

'Yes, it is my sister, Athene,' said Quicksilver. 'We could not make this journey without her. Besides, she has better eyes than either of us. Why, she can see you now, just as though you were not invisible! She will be the first to discover the Gorgons.'

By this time they were flying over the ocean. Far below, Perseus could see the white waves rolling on the shores of the beaches and foaming against the rocky cliffs.

Just then a quiet voice spoke in the air beside him.

'Perseus,' said the voice, 'there are the Gorgons.'

'Where?' asked Perseus. 'I cannot see them.'

'On the shore of that island below us,' replied the voice.

'I told you she would be the first to discover them!' said Quicksilver.

Looking down, Perseus could see a small island with the sea breaking into white foam around its rocky shore. On one side there was a sandy beach. They flew down towards it.

Then Perseus saw the Gorgons. Their fearful golden metal was shining in the moonlight. They were asleep; and they lay on the sand like giant dragon-flies or huge beetles, with their brassy claws stretched out as if they were tearing a poor creature to pieces in their dreams.

Yet there was something human about these terrible Gorgons, too. It was a horrible sight to see the snakes like hair on their heads, twisting and turning and putting out their poisoned tongues. Luckily the heads of the Gorgons were turned away from Perseus, for if he had looked directly at their faces he would have fallen out of the air, turned to stone.

'Now is the time!' whispered Quicksilver. 'Be quick, for if one of the Gorgons wakes you are too late!'

'Which is Medusa?' asked Perseus, drawing his sword and flying a little lower. 'All three look alike to me!'

Medusa was the only one whose head could be cut off. The other two Gorgons had a far stronger covering of iron which never could be cut, not even with a magic sword.

'Be careful!' said the calm voice at his side.

17

' One of the Gorgons is moving in her sleep and going to turn over. That is Medusa. Remember not to look at her! Look at her reflection in the bright shield.'

Now Perseus understood why he had been told to polish the shield. He looked into it and saw the Gorgon's face. It was the most fierce and terrible face that ever was seen. The hundred hissing snakes that twisted themselves over the forehead made it even more horrible. The eyes were closed, as Medusa still slept, but Perseus could see her tiger's tusks as she opened her mouth, and she spread her terrible brazen claws on the sand.

' Now—make a dash!' said Quicksilver.

' But be calm,' said the quiet voice. ' Look in your shield as you fly down, and take care that you do not miss with your first stroke.'

Perseus flew downwards, keeping his eyes on Medusa's image in the shield. As he came closer to the monster, each horrible snake stretched out its head and Medusa awoke. But she awoke too late. The sword was very sharp and Perseus used it with the speed of a flash of lightning. The head of the Gorgon Medusa fell from her body.

' Well done!' cried Quicksilver. ' Quick! Put the head in the magic wallet.'

As soon as Perseus took hold of the wallet, which he had hung round his neck, he was amazed to find that it was suddenly large enough to contain the

Perseus flew downwards, keeping his eyes on Medusa's image
in the shield

horrible head. He quickly pushed it into the wallet.

' Your task is done,' said the calm voice. ' Now fly, for the other Gorgons are waking.'

Perseus flew upwards just in time. The other two Gorgons made a terrible noise when they saw Medusa's body lying headless on the sand. The snakes on their heads hissed horribly as they rose, and Medusa's snakes answered them from inside the magic wallet.

The angry Gorgons flew up into the air, their

terrible teeth showing and their great brass claws waving as they flew. They shook their huge wings wildly and circled the dead Medusa, looking for their enemy so that they might turn him to stone.

But Perseus wore the helmet of invisibility and the Gorgons could not see him. He was careful not to look at these two monsters as they came near him. He also wore the winged slippers and so he was able to fly upwards very quickly. He was a mile or more above the Gorgons in a flash, and at that height the screams of the terrible creatures soon faded away. He flew straight towards the island of Seriphus, to carry Medusa's head to the king.

Several other wonderful adventures happened to Perseus on his way home. He rescued a beautiful maiden called Andromeda from a terrible sea-monster; and he changed a wicked giant into a mountain of stone, by showing him the Gorgon's head. If you go to Africa one day, you can see the very mountain still standing there, which is called by the giant's name, Atlas.

At last, Perseus arrived at the island of Seriphus, where he went first to see his mother. But he found that in his absence the wicked king had treated Danaë so cruelly that she had escaped to a temple, where the good priests took care of her.

These priests and the kind-hearted fisherman seem to have been the only people on the island who cared about doing right. The rest of the people, and the king himself, deserved the sad fate that was in store for them.

Not finding his mother, Perseus went straight to the palace, where he was taken at once to the king.

Polydectes was not pleased to see him. He had thought, in his evil mind, that the Gorgons would tear the young man to pieces. However, he made the best of it and asked Perseus if he had brought the head of Medusa. ' If not,' the king said, ' you will be punished, for I must have that head for my bridal present.'

' Yes, your Majesty,' Perseus answered in a quiet voice, as if he had done nothing wonderful, ' I have brought you the Gorgon's Head, with its hissing snakes.'

' Then let me see it,' said Polydectes. ' It must be a curious sight, if the stories about it are true.'

' It is,' said Perseus. ' In fact, it is a sight that will fix the eyes of all who see it. I suggest that there is a public holiday, so that all of your Majesty's people may see this wonderful thing. Few of them will have seen a Gorgon's head before, and they may never see one again.'

The king knew that his people were idle, always ready for a public holiday. So he sent out his messengers with trumpets, to call them all to the palace to see the head of the Gorgon.

A great crowd was soon on its way. If there were any good people we have not yet heard about they must have stayed quietly at home, minding their own business and looking after the children. Most of the people ran as fast as they could to the palace, pushing and elbowing their way towards a balcony where Perseus stood ready, with the wallet in his hand.

On a platform near the balcony sat King Polydectes, with his ministers and the men of his court. Below them stood the people; and every eye was on Perseus.

'Show us the head! Show us the head!' they all cried. There was a fierceness and cruelty in their cry, as if they might tear Perseus to pieces if he didn't obey them at once. 'Show us the head of Medusa,' they cried again.

A feeling of sorrow and pity came over Perseus.

'O King!' he cried, 'O people! I do not want to show you this hateful thing!'

'Coward! Traitor!' yelled the people, madly. 'He has tricked us—he has not got the Gorgon's head! Show us the head, if you have it—or we will have your own!'

The ministers and the men of the court whispered to the king. King Polydectes lifted up his hand and ordered Perseus to obey.

'Show us the head at once, or you die!' said the king.

'Then—here it is!' cried Perseus, in a voice like a trumpet, as he held up the dreadful sight.

At once, as every eye looked upon the head of Medusa, so were they all fixed for ever in a wide stony stare. The wicked King Polydectes, his ministers, his men of the court and all his people, were turned at once into figures of stone, never to move again.

Perseus put the Gorgon's head back into the magic wallet. He went to tell his mother that it was safe to leave the temple where she was staying; she need not fear the wicked King Polydectes ever again.

2. THE GOLDEN TOUCH

LONG ago, there lived a very rich man called Midas. Besides being rich he was a king, and he had a little daughter called Marygold.

King Midas loved gold more than anything else in the world.   He liked being a king, chiefly because he loved his golden crown.   He loved his daughter dearly, too, and the more he loved her the more gold he wanted for her sake.

When King Midas saw the golden light of the sun at evening, he wished it could turn everything into real gold.   When Marygold came to him with a bunch of sweet yellow flowers, he would say, ' If they were as golden as they look, they would be worth picking!'   Even the roses in his garden did not please him any more—the largest and sweetest and most beautiful roses ever seen—because they were not made of gold.   And although the king was very fond of music in his youth, the only music he loved now was the sound of gold coins, one against another.

At last, King Midas could not bear to touch anything that was not gold.   He used to go down to a secret room under his palace where he kept his precious store.   He would lock himself in and count his gold pieces.   He would hold the bars of gold,

24

and admire his gold cups and plates, until he could hardly bear to leave them.

Now, in those days a great many wonderful things used to happen, just as they do today. One morning King Midas was in his treasure-room when he noticed that the sun was shining into the room more brightly than usual. Not only that, but a stranger stood there, smiling at him in the light of the sunbeam.

King Midas knew that he had locked himself in as usual, and so he guessed that his visitor was no ordinary person.

The stranger looked at the gold pieces that the

A stranger stood there, smiling at him in the light of the sunbeam

king was counting. 'You seem to be a very rich man!' he said.

ı' But it has taken me a long time to collect this gold,' said King Midas. ' If I could live a thousand years, I might have time to get richer.'

' What! Aren't you satisfied?' asked the stranger. ' What else do you want?'

Midas thought carefully. This was a wonderful chance, and he felt that the stranger had magical powers.

' I am tired of collecting my riches so slowly,' he said. ' I wish everything I touch could be turned into gold!'

' The Golden Touch!' exclaimed the stranger. ' Are you sure you would never regret it?'

' How could I regret such a thing?' said Midas. ' It would give me perfect happiness at last.'

' Very well, then,' the stranger said, as he turned to go. ' Tomorrow at sunrise you will find that you have the Golden Touch.'

The light of the sunbeam brightened so vividly that Midas closed his eyes. When he opened them again, the stranger had gone.

Next morning, King Midas awoke before the dawn. He looked eagerly to see if his bed had been turned into gold. But no; it was exactly as it had been before. He lay, very disappointed, looking around his room.

Suddenly, the earliest sunbeam of the rising sun

shone through the window and up to the ceiling above. It seemed to reflect its golden light towards him. Looking at the sheet on his bed, Midas was astonished to find that it had become cloth of gold! The Golden Touch had truly come to him, with the first sunbeam!

King Midas got out of bed in excitement. He touched one of the legs of the bed as he did so— and it immediately became a golden pillar! He pulled the curtain at the window, and it at once became golden, too! He put on his clothes, and found himself dressed in golden cloth!

He took up his spectacles and put them on—and he found he could see nothing at all. The glasses had turned into gold and he could not see through them. He took them off again.

' Never mind,' he thought to himself. ' The Golden Touch is worth more than a pair of spectacles, and Marygold will be able to read to me.'

King Midas went downstairs and into the garden. He noticed that even the brass handle of the door became gold at once as he turned it. Then he went among the rose-trees that had always been his pride and joy in the past.

When he went in to breakfast that morning, he felt more hungry than usual. While he was waiting for his eggs to be ready, little Marygold came in, crying bitterly.

27

'Look, father!' she cried, holding out a golden rose. 'I went to pick you some roses and they are yellow and hard, and their sweet scent is gone!'

'Never mind, my dear,' said her father. 'They are worth much more like that. Sit down and eat your breakfast.'

He poured himself a cup of coffee as he spoke. The coffee pot was a golden one when he put it back on the table. Then he tried a spoonful of coffee, to see if it was sweet enough. But it had become liquid gold!

'Well!' he exclaimed. He was thirsty.

'What is the matter, father?' asked Marygold.

'Nothing, child. Drink your milk,' Midas said.

But the eggs that he tried to eat, the fish, the bread, the butter—all the food was uneatable for the king, that morning!

'How am I to have any breakfast?' he thought. 'Such costly food is before me, and I can eat nothing!'

He looked across the table at Marygold. She was eating happily, her tears forgotten. She looked up, saw that something was wrong, and came round to comfort her father.

'What is wrong, father?' she asked.

Midas bent down and kissed his little daughter.

Then—what a terrible change came over Marygold! Her sweet little face turned to yellow gold, her lovely hair became golden metal, her little body hardened into a figure of solid gold. What had he done?

This story would be too sad for us all if we lingered too long on this terrible sight. King Midas could not bear to look at Marygold; yet he could not leave her side. He felt so sad and sorrowful that he wished he was the poorest man in all the world, if only his beloved daughter could be herself again.

In despair, Midas looked about him. Suddenly he saw the stranger that had visited him the day before.

'Well, Midas,' said the stranger. 'How do you like having the Golden Touch?'

'I have lost everything I really loved,' said King Midas. 'I am full of sorrow and regret. Gold is of no use to me now.'

'So you have learnt something since yesterday?' asked the stranger. 'Now, which is worth more— the Golden Touch or a cup of cold water?'

'Oh, blessed water!' exclaimed Midas. 'Will I ever taste it again?'

'The Golden Touch—or a piece of bread?' the stranger said.

'A piece of bread,' answered Midas, ' is worth all the gold on earth!'

'Gold—or your own little daughter?' asked the stranger.

'Oh—my child, my child!' cried poor Midas.

' I would not have given one hair of her head for the power to change the whole earth into gold!'

The stranger looked seriously at King Midas.

' You are wiser than you were,' he said. ' Your heart is still flesh and blood. You know truly that the common things of life, which are within everyone's reach, are more valuable than riches. Tell me, do you want to keep the Golden Touch?'

' No, it is hateful to me now,' said Midas, passionately.

A fly settled on the king's nose and immediately fell to the floor, a small scrap of gold. Midas shuddered.

' Then go down to the end of your garden,' said the stranger, ' and wash yourself in the water of the river there. Then bring some of the same water and sprinkle it over anything that you wish to change back again. If you do this, truly and sincerely, you can set right again the results of your greed of gold.'

King Midas bowed his head. When he looked up again, the stranger had vanished.

The king ran at once to the river. Without waiting to take off his clothes, he dived in. In the coolness of the water, he felt at once that a weight had been lifted from his heart and body.

He came out of the river. He was free of the Golden Touch! He put out his hand and touched a wild rose on the river's bank, and he found with thankfulness that it remained the same sweet flower. Taking up a water pot, he quickly filled it with river water and took it back to the palace.

I expect the servants thought it very strange to see their royal master carrying a water pot; but that water was more precious to Midas than an ocean of gold.

The king went straight to the golden figure of little Marygold. As he sprinkled the water on her,

As he sprinkled the water on her, the rosy colour came back to her cheeks

the rosy colour came back to her cheeks. She began to sneeze and shake the water from her golden hair.

'Oh, father! See how wet I am—and my dress was clean this morning!' she said.

Marygold did not know what had happened to her, and her father did not tell her how wrong and foolish he had been. He took her out into the garden, where they watered the flowers together and picked a bunch of sweetly-scented roses.

3. PANDORA AND THE BOX

THOUSANDS of years ago, the world was very different from what it is now. In those days everyone was a child. No fathers or mothers were needed to look after the children, because there was no danger or trouble of any kind. No cooking had to be done and no clothes had to be mended. Whenever a child wanted something to eat he found it growing on a tree.

What was most wonderful of all, the children never quarrelled and they never cried. In fact, those ugly little creatures called Troubles had never been seen. They never flew about as they do nowadays, like horrid mosquitoes, making everyone unhappy.

Life was very pleasant in those days. There was no hard work and no unhappiness; nothing but games and dances and the sweet laughter of children all day long.

But that was before Pandora came to live with Epimetheus and be his playmate.

When she came into the cottage where Epimetheus lived, the first thing Pandora saw was a big box. It stood on the floor and got in the way, but Epimetheus would not say where it had come from or what was in it.

33

As the days went by, Pandora enjoyed the games with the other children and eating her food off the trees, but she could not forget the mysterious box in the cottage. She was very curious about it.

'Where did it come from? What is inside?' she asked Epimetheus again and again.

'Do not ask questions, Pandora,' said Epimetheus. 'It is a secret. The box was left here for me to take care of and I do not know what is in it. Come outside and play with the others.'

But the next day, and the next day, and the day after that, Pandora thought of nothing but the secret box. At last, Epimetheus told her that it had been brought to him by a smiling person who wore a cap with feathers on it.

'What sort of staff did he have?' asked Pandora.

'It was a long stick that had two serpents twisting round it,' he answered, 'and it was carved so cleverly that I thought they were real.'

'It must have been Quicksilver,' Pandora said. 'He is the only one with a staff like that. It was he who brought me here, too. Perhaps there are toys and pretty dresses for me in the box, or something nice for us to eat!'

'Perhaps so,' said Epimetheus, as he turned to go out to play again, 'but, until he comes back and tells us so, we must not touch the box.'

'What a dull boy he is!' said Pandora to herself

when he had gone. ' I do wish he would take more interest in things.'

When she was alone in the cottage she stood looking at the mysterious box for a long time. It was made of a beautiful dark wood, which was so polished that Pandora could see her face in it. There was carving on the sides and corners, in a wonderful design of flowers and fruit. Here and there a face looked out from among the leaves. In the centre of the polished lid there was the most lovely face of all, and it seemed to smile at Pandora.

' Why don't you open the box?' it seemed to say to her. ' What harm can there be? You may find something lovely inside!'

Pandora stooped down and tried to lift one end of the big box, but it was too heavy for her. She looked at the lid again.

There was no lock. The box was fastened by a gold cord which was tied in a mysterious knot. Several times Pandora had touched this knot and looked closely at it, but it seemed to have no beginning and no end.

Through the open window Pandora could hear the voices of happy children, playing in the sunshine. It was a lovely day. Why not leave this mysterious box and go out to play with the others?

But her fingers were busy with the knot in the golden cord, and the lovely face on the lid of the box seemed to smile at her more mysteriously than ever.

Just then, Pandora twisted the golden cord and it seemed to undo itself as if by magic. The knot was undone.

'What will Epimetheus say?' thought Pandora. 'I must tie it again, quickly!'

But she could not remember what the knot was like, and the gold cord seemed to refuse to be tied again.

'When Epimetheus comes in, he will see that the cord is untied,' she said to herself, 'and he will never believe that I have not looked inside!'

Pandora seemed to hear little voices calling to her from inside the box. 'Let us out, Pandora! We will play with you—only let us out!'

Why not look into the box, just once? She put her hand on the lid.

Just at that moment, Epimetheus came back to the door of the cottage. If he had cried out and stopped Pandora, the contents of the box would never have been known. He saw at once that Pandora was opening the box, but he was really just as curious about it as she was. He stood still by the door.

As Pandora raised the lid, the cottage became dark and there was the sound of thunder overhead. When she looked inside the box, a cloud of winged creatures flew out into the room. Epimetheus cried out in pain.

A cloud of winged creatures flew out into the room

' Oh—I am stung! Oh, Pandora, why did you open the box?'

The tiny creatures, like angry mosquitoes, began to buzz round the room and sting them both. Pandora screamed and began to cry.

By lifting the lid of the mysterious box she had let out all the Troubles of the world. She had set free all the Cares, Diseases and Sorrows that had been safely shut up in the box so that happy children might never know such things.

Not only that, but the winged Troubles flew out of the cottage and they began to sting all the other children. No one smiled for a long time after this;

and instead of remaining young, they grew older day by day. Besides that, all the flowers began to fade and die, which they had never done before.

Pandora and Epimetheus stayed in the cottage, both in much pain. It was the first pain that had ever been felt since the world began, and this made it hurt all the more. Besides, they were both very cross; with themselves and with each other.

Pandora sat on the floor with her head against the fatal box, crying bitterly. She knew how naughty she had been. Epimetheus sat in a corner of the room with his back to her. He knew he was almost as much to blame as she was.

Suddenly there was a little tap from inside the box.

'What was that?' said Pandora, lifting her head.

Again there came the little tap, as if a tiny fairy hand was knocking on the inside of the lid.

'Who are you?' called Pandora, her curiosity returning.

'Lift the lid and you shall see,' said a sweet little voice.

'No, no!' answered Pandora, beginning to cry again. 'I have had enough of lifting the lid!'

'But I am not like those horrid creatures with stings in their tails,' said the little voice. 'Let me out, Pandora, and you won't regret it.'

Pandora turned to Epimetheus. 'Shall I open the box again?' she asked him.

' Well, you have let out so many Troubles already,' he said. ' I suppose one more won't make any difference.'

' Unkind boy!' cried the little voice inside the box. ' He knows that he is longing to see me. Come, Pandora, lift up the lid. If only you will let me out into the fresh air, I will comfort you.'

' I must open the box—come what may!' cried Pandora.

' And I will help you!' Epimetheus said, as he ran across the room.

They lifted the lid of the box together.

Out flew a sunny little fairy-like creature that brought light wherever she went! Have you ever seen the sunshine dance on a mirror? The little sunny creature was just like that. She kissed Pandora's forehead, and all the pain was gone at once! She flew to Epimetheus, and the stings of the Troubles hurt him no more.

Then the little fairy creature looked at them so sweetly that they were both very glad that they had opened the box this time.

' Tell us—who are you?' asked Pandora.

' I am called Hope,' answered the sunny little person. ' I was put into the box to help the human race to bear the pain of all those horrid Troubles.'

' Your wings seem to have all the colours of the rainbow!' exclaimed Pandora.

' Yes, they are like the rainbow,' said Hope, ' for I am made of tears as well as smiles.'

' And will you stay with us for ever and ever?' asked Epimetheus.

' As long as you need me,' said Hope, smiling at them. ' I promise that I will never leave you. There may be times when I seem to disappear, but when you least expect me you will see the light of my wings.'

The children found that her words were true. Although the Troubles still continued to fly about the world, hurting everyone with their stings, yet the sunshine of Hope was never far away.

And isn't it true today? What should we all do without Hope? Hope lightens the heaviest of Troubles. Hope gives new life to the troubled world. Hope makes all things new.

4. PEGASUS, THE WINGED HORSE

ONCE, long ago, in the land of Greece, a young man came to rest at a pleasant spot at sunset. He drank from the cool and sparkling water that flowed from the hill-side into a fountain.

'What is the name of this fountain?' he asked a maiden who was filling her water-pot.

'It is called the Fountain of Pirene,' answered the maiden. 'They say that the water came from the sorrow of a mother's heart. Her tears never stopped flowing after the death of her beloved son.'

'So this is the Fountain of Pirene!' said the young man. 'I have come a long way to find it.'

A farmer, who had brought his cows to drink, then spoke.

'I see you are carrying a bridle[1], young man. Have you lost your horse?'

'No,' said Bellerophon, for that was the young man's name, 'but I am looking for one that is famous—the winged horse, Pegasus. They say that he comes to drink at this fountain.'

'The winged horse!' laughed the farmer. 'Surely you don't believe that old tale of a winged horse! He would never do the farm work as well as a cart horse, anyway.'

---

1. *bridle:* usually made of leather, and placed over a horse's head.

Bellerophon turned to an old grey man who stood near.

'But you, sir?' he asked. 'You must have seen this horse in your younger days?'

'Ah, my memory is not good these days,' said the old grey man. 'I used to believe in this horse when I was young, but now I never think of such things.'

'And you, fair maiden?' asked Bellerophon. 'You could see Pegasus with your bright eyes, if anyone can!'

'I thought I saw him, once,' the maiden said, with a smile and a blush. 'It was either Pegasus or a large white bird, very high in the sky. And once, here at the fountain, I heard a neigh[2]—but I could see no horse then.'

Bellerophon turned to a little boy who had been gazing at him all this time in silence.

'And you, my little fellow? I suppose you have often seen Pegasus?'

'Why, yes, I have,' said the child at once. 'I saw him yesterday—and many times before.'

Bellerophon took the boy aside to sit on the grass with him. 'Come and tell me all about it,' he said.

'You see,' said the child, 'I often come to sail my boat in the fountain. Sometimes, when I look down into the water, I see the white winged horse

---

2. *neigh:* Pronounced 'nay'—the sound a horse makes to attract attention.

reflected there when he flies in the sky. Then I wish he would come down and take me up to the moon, riding on his back. But if I turn to look at him, he flies away.'

Bellerophon decided to put his faith in the child, who had seen Pegasus reflected in the water; and in the maiden, who had heard him neigh. He stayed near the fountain for days, looking up at the sky and down into the water, hoping to see the winged horse. He held the bridle always ready; that bridle with its bright rows of gems and the golden bit[3].

The country people laughed at Bellerophon when they saw him there. They offered to sell him a horse if he wanted one. They also tried to buy the beautiful bridle, but Bellerophon would have nothing to do with them. He continued to watch and wait near the fountain.

It was the most important thing in the world to Bellerophon, that he should find the winged horse. He wished with all his heart to rid a neighbouring country of a terrible monster that was frightening everyone there, and a winged horse would be the best possible aid in attacking it.

In those days, a young man counted it the highest honour to fight giants and dragons and other wild beasts, and so to protect his friends. In Lycia, the neighbouring country, the king had asked

---

3. *bit:* A metal piece attached to the bridle and placed in a horse's mouth to control it.

Bellerophon to save his people from a monster more terrible than any that had ever been seen there.

This monster was called the Chimaera. It was fierce and swift, ugly and poisonous; the hardest creature to fight and the most difficult to run away from.

Its tail was like that of a giant snake, and it had three heads. One was of a lion, one was of a goat and the third was that of a poisonous snake. Flaming fire came out of all three mouths at once. The Chimaera ran like a lion and a goat, and it wriggled along like a snake; so that it was as fast as all three together.

With its flaming breath, the Chimaera could set fire to a forest. It could burn up a harvest of corn or destroy a village. It used to eat people and animals alive and cook them in its stomach, which was a burning oven.

Bellerophon knew that he must have the swiftest horse in the world to fight this Chimaera, and what horse could be better than the winged horse, Pegasus? It was true that a lot of people did not believe in it, but Bellerophon was certain that the horse was real.

This was why he had travelled all the way from Lycia to Greece, and this was why he had brought the beautiful bridle with him. It was a magic bridle. If he could put it on Pegasus, the winged horse would obey him at once and fly wherever he chose.

But it was a weary wait. Bellerophon might have given up hope entirely, if it had not been for the faith of the little child.

' I think we shall see Pegasus today!' the boy would say, looking up at him hopefully.

But Bellerophon was anxious. He knew that the Chimaera was doing much damage in Lycia while he waited there at the fountain. He began to think he would be an old man before Pegasus came, and then he would have no strength left to fight the monster.

One morning, the little boy seemed to be more hopeful than usual. ' Dear Bellerophon,' he cried. ' I feel sure that we shall see Pegasus today!'

He did not leave Bellerophon's side all that day. They ate a crust of bread together and drank some water out of the fountain. Then they sat by the water in the shade of the trees.

Suddenly, Bellerophon felt the child's hand in his. He heard a soft whisper, ' See there—in the fountain, Bellerophon!'

In the mirror of the shining water, Bellerophon thought he saw the reflection of a bird, high in the sky, with the sunshine bright on its silvery wings.

' It is no bird!' whispered the child. ' It is the winged horse, Pegasus!'

Bellerophon's heart began to beat fast. He

45

caught the child in his arms and stepped back into the deep shade of the trees. If Pegasus saw them, he might fly away. Now they could look up at the bright wings that flew in a circle high above them. It really was the winged horse, white and beautiful, coming at last to drink at the fountain of Pirene.

Downward came Pegasus, with his wide and silvery wings spread in the sunshine. He flew lower and lower, until at last his feet lightly touched the grass round the fountain and he folded his wings.

Stooping his beautiful white head, the winged horse drank deep of the fountain. He drew in the

Downward came Pegasus

water with long sighs and pauses, taking another drink and yet another until he was satisfied, for he loved this sweet water of Pirene more than any other.

Then he tasted the honey-flowers of the clover that grew by the water and turned to run on the grass. For Pegasus was gay and playful, and, although he could fly so high and so far, he liked to run on the ground just for the fun of it. He fluttered his great wings as lightly as a bird, running little races, half on earth and half in air, until Bellerophon and the child thought they had never seen anything so wild and free and beautiful as this wonderful winged horse. It seemed a sin to think of putting a bridle on him.

Soon the white horse folded his wings again and lay down on the soft green grass. He rolled over on his back, as horses do, with his four slender white legs in the air. Bellerophon and the child held their breath with delight to see him do this.

When Pegasus had had enough of rolling over and over he put out his two fore-legs, like any other horse, ready to get up again.

Bellerophon had been waiting for this moment. With a quick run he left the shade of the trees and jumped on to the horse's back. Yes—there he was, sitting on the winged horse!

When Pegasus felt the weight of a man on his back for the first time, he leapt into the air. Bellerophon found himself five hundred feet up in an instant, while Pegasus snorted and shook with terror. Then the horse went through the wildest antics that had ever been seen, trying all the time to throw Bellerophon off his back.

Pegasus twisted himself sideways and backwards; he stood on his hind legs; then he put his head between his fore-legs and kicked out behind, with his wings pointing upwards. When he was about two miles from the earth he turned a somersault, and Bellerophon's heels were suddenly where his head had been. Then Pegasus turned his head and tried to bite his rider, fire flashing from his eyes. He fluttered his wings so wildly that one of the silver feathers floated down to the ground, where the little boy picked it up and kept it as long as he lived, in memory of Pegasus and Bellerophon.

But Bellerophon was a good horseman. There came a chance at last to put the magic bridle on Pegasus, and he did not miss his chance. No sooner was the golden bit between his teeth than Pegasus became as docile as if he had always eaten his food out of Bellerophon's hand.

It was almost sad to see such a wild and wonderful creature suddenly become so tame, and Pegasus seemed to feel sad too. He looked round at Bellerophon with tears in his beautiful eyes instead of flashing fire. But when Bellerophon patted his head and spoke kindly to him, another look came into the eyes of Pegasus.   He was glad, after being so long alone, to find that he had a master and a friend.

Meanwhile, they had come a long way.   Pegasus had turned towards the mountain called Helicon and at last he alighted on its summit.   Bellerophon knew that this was where Pegasus had his home. He got down from the horse's back.   He thought of the free life that Pegasus had always lived and he did not want to keep him against his will.

Bellerophon took the bridle from the horse's head. ' Leave me, Pegasus,' he said.   ' Leave me, or love me.'

In an instant the winged horse spread his wings and flew straight upwards from the top of the mountain.   It was now twilight on Mount Helicon, but Pegasus flew so high that the light of the setting sun shone on him as he disappeared into the wide spaces of the evening sky.

Bellerophon was afraid that Pegasus would not come back, but the bright wings appeared once more and the horse returned to him.   He would not leave his master again.

That night they lay down to sleep together, and Bellerophon's arm was round the neck of Pegasus. In the morning they awoke at dawn and said good-morning to each other, each in his own language.

For several days Bellerophon and Pegasus went for journeys in the sky together, getting to know each other. A thousand miles a day was nothing to Pegasus, and so they visited many distant countries. They sometimes went so high that the earth looked no bigger than the moon! It was always sunny weather above the clouds, and Bellerophon would have liked to live in this delightful way for ever. But he remembered the horrible Chimaera which he had promised to kill.

At last, Bellerophon was quite used to riding high in the air, and he had taught Pegasus to obey his slightest touch. So he decided that the time had come for him to go on his dangerous adventure.

That night they slept by a spring called Hippocrene, and at dawn they awoke as usual. After they had drunk of the sparkling water of the spring, Pegasus held out his head as usual so that his master might put on his bridle. Then, with many playful leaps and bounds, he showed that he was eager to be off.

Bellerophon put on his sword and hung his shield from his shoulders, making himself ready for battle. Then he mounted; and in a second Pegasus was five miles above the earth, so that they could see their way more clearly. Bellerophon turned Pegasus towards the east and they soon found themselves over the rocky hills and valleys of Lycia.

Hiding themselves low in a cloud, they looked for some sign of the monster. Below they could see the ruins of houses that had been burnt, and the bodies of dead cattle in the fields.

'The Chimaera must have done this,' thought Bellerophon. 'But where is the cave where the monster lives?'

Looking about, he saw smoke coming from a valley not far away. He made a sign and Pegasus understood, taking his rider within a few yards of the ground. It was not long before they came to the opening of a cave in the hill-side, where three separate puffs of smoke seemed to come from within. Looking into the cave, Bellerophon saw the three-headed monster, the heads of the lion, the goat and the snake breathing smoke. Pegasus saw it too and his neigh sounded like a battle-cry.

At this sound the three heads lifted themselves and sent out fierce flames. The monster sprang out of the cave towards them, its huge claws stretched upward, its three heads lifted. It was only the speed of Pegasus that saved Bellerophon, for the winged horse was high in the air in a flash and out of the monster's reach.

Bellerophon drew his sword and whispered to his horse. 'Help me to slay this monster, Pegasus, or you will fly back to Helicon alone!'

Pegasus turned his head and rubbed his nose softly against his master's cheek. It was his way of saying he would never leave his master.

Then he flew down as swift as an arrow, attacking

51

Bellerophon made a cut with his sword as he passed the Chimaera

the monster from the side.   Bellerophon made a cut
with his sword as he passed the Chimaera.   When
they were safely out of danger again, he turned and
saw that he had cut off the goat's head.   But the
heads of the snake and the lion seemed to send out
more flame and fury than before, as they hissed and
roared together.

' Now, my brave Pegasus!' cried Bellerophon.
' Another stroke like that!'

He shook the bridle and Pegasus flew down again
as swiftly as before.   Bellerophon aimed at the two
heads with his sword, but this time he did not escape

so easily. The Chimaera clawed him on the shoulder as they passed, and the left wing of Pegasus was damaged.

Turning to look, Bellerophon could see that he had struck off the lion's head. Only the head of the snake was left; but the flame from its mouth was more fierce than ever, and it reached for fully five hundred yards.

Fifty miles away, the King of Lycia heard the hisses of the snake, so loud and fierce that he trembled with fear.

The winged horse paused in the air and neighed angrily.

' Are you hurt, my Pegasus?' cried Bellerophon. ' The Chimaera shall pay for it, with his last head!'

Then he shook the bridle again and shouted loudly. This time he guided Pegasus straight at the monster, and for a moment it seemed that they were lost in its flaming breath. The heat of the fire scorched the wings of Pegasus. The hair on one side of Bellerophon's head was scorched too, although they were still a hundred yards away from the monster.

And then the worst happened. The Chimaera suddenly sprang at Pegasus and clung to him with all its strength, winding its snaky tail round him. Bellerophon held up his shield to protect himself from the monster's breath. Up flew the winged horse swiftly, carrying its young rider and his terrible enemy, above the mountains and above the clouds.

Perhaps the best way to fight a Chimaera is to get as close to it as possible. The Chimaera was so mad with pain and rage that it did not guard itself. As it tried to get its claws into Bellerophon it left its breast unprotected. Seeing this, the young man drove his sword into its heart with all his might.

The Chimaera let go of Pegasus and fell downwards from that great height. As it fell, the fire within its stomach flamed more fiercely than ever, burning it to ashes.

Those who saw the flaming body fall to earth thought it was a comet, but on the following day the farmers found two strange sights in the fields. They saw several acres of blackened ashes, and a heap of whitened bones as high as a house—it was the end of the Chimaera.

When Bellerophon saw that victory was won, he bent forward and kissed his horse, patting the arched white neck.

' Back now, Pegasus!' he said. ' Back to the Fountain of Pirene!'

Pegasus flew through the air more quickly than ever, and they were soon at the fountain. When they had refreshed themselves in the clear and life-giving water, Bellerophon saw that the old grey man had come again to the fountain. He looked at Pegasus and nodded his grey head.

' I remember now,' the old man said. ' I did

see this winged horse once, when I was a boy. But he was ten times more beautiful in those days!'

There was the sound of running feet and the little boy came to Bellerophon. 'You have won the battle!' he cried. 'I knew you would!'

'Yes, I won,' said Bellerophon. 'But without your faith I should not have waited for Pegasus; I should never have ridden him high above the clouds, nor have conquered the terrible Chimaera. You helped me most of all!'

He went to where the winged horse was drinking at the fountain and took off the bridle. 'Go home, now, Pegasus,' he said. 'Be free for evermore!'

But Pegasus rested his head on Bellerophon's shoulder and would not leave him.

'Very well, then, Pegasus,' said Bellerophon, patting the beautiful white head. 'You shall stay with me as long as you like; and first we will go and tell the King of Lycia how we killed the monster Chimaera.'

Then Bellorophon said farewell to the child, and he promised to come back to him after he had been to Lycia.

And in later years, it was the child who rode even further on Pegasus than Bellerophon had done, and he did even more mighty deeds than the slaying of the monster Chimaera.

For he grew to be a poet, and his flights were flights of imagination.

5. ANTAEUS AND THE PYGMIES

A LONG time ago, when the world was even more full of wonders than it is now, there lived a giant named Antaeus. Near him lived several millions of tiny little people who were called Pygmies.

The giant and the Pygmies were children of the same Mother Earth, and they lived happily next door to each other in the middle of hot Africa.

The giant was the biggest possible figure of a man and the Pygmies had to use a telescope to see the top of him. In misty weather they could see only his legs, but in sunny weather Antaeus was a very fine sight indeed, with his one great eye in the middle of his forehead which was as big as a cart wheel. He could give a friendly wink to the whole of the Pygmy nation at once.

The little people of the Pygmy race were no bigger than a few inches. If one of them grew to be eight inches high he was considered to be a very tall man indeed. The little streets of the Pygmy towns were about three feet wide, with tiny houses as small as a bird cage. The highest temple was no higher than a table, and the little fields of the Pygmy farmers were the size of flower beds. A whole family of them could sleep in a shoe, and you could easily hide one of the Pygmy babies in a thimble.

The giant Antaeus was so tall that he carried a pine-tree as a walking stick, and it was eight feet thick.

The Pygmies were so small, that when they cut their wheat at harvest time they had to run and get out of the way when it fell, or it might knock them down!

The little people loved to talk to Antaeus, and they would often call up to him as loud as they could, ' Hello, brother Antaeus, how are you?'

When the tiny sound of their voices reached him, the giant would say, ' Quite well, thank you, brother Pygmies,'—and the thunder of his giant voice would nearly make their walls fall down, only they were made so cleverly with plastered clay and feathers and straw.

It was good fortune for the Pygmies that Antaeus was their friend, for he had more strength in his little finger than in ten million of their little bodies. He could have destroyed their biggest city with one kick of his foot; and with one breath he could have blown them all away, houses and inhabitants included.

But, being a son of Mother Earth as they all were, Antaeus loved the Pygmies with as big a love as it was possible to feel for such tiny creatures. The Pygmies, in their turn, loved the giant with as much love as their little hearts could hold.

Antaeus was always ready to help the Pygmies in

any way he could. For instance, if they wanted a good breeze to turn their wind-mills, he just breathed as usual and turned his head in the right direction. And when the sun was too hot for them, as it often was, he sat himself down and let his shadow cover their whole country. But as for matters in general, he was wise enough to leave them to manage their own affairs—which is about the best thing that great people can do for small ones.

It is a pleasant picture to imagine, the giant Antaeus standing among the Pygmies like the tallest tower that ever was built, while they ran about like tiny ants round his feet. In fact, the giant needed the little people to play with, more than the Pygmies needed him, for without them he hadn't a friend in the world.

No other giant like Antaeus had ever been created and so he had never had a friend of his own size to talk to. When he stood with his head among the clouds he was quite alone, and he had been so for hundreds of years. Even if he had met another giant he would have fought him at once; but with the Pygmies he was the kindest and merriest old giant that ever washed his face in a cloud.

His little friends had a great opinion of their own importance, like many other small people, and they were sometimes quite sorry for Antaeus because he was so big.

' Poor giant!' they would say to each other. ' We must be kind to him. He has a dull time up there all by himself. He needs us to cheer him up!'

On their holidays the Pygmies had excellent sports. They would run their races over the giant. When he stretched himself out on the ground he looked like a range of hills, and it was a good hour's walk to travel from his head to his feet. The children used to play in his hair or his beard. Some of the boys ran races on his forehead, to see which of them could be first round the circle of his one big eye.

When Antaeus lay with his head on one side, they would march up to the huge cave of his mouth and peep into it, running away with tiny screams when he pretended to swallow fifty of them at once. Then they would prick his skin with their tiny swords and spears, to see how thick it was. In fact, they were sometimes as troublesome as a swarm of mosquitoes, but Antaeus did not often get cross with the Pygmies.

One day, the mighty Antaeus was resting at full length among his little friends. His pine-tree walking stick lay by his side. His head was in one part of the country and his feet were across the boundaries of another part, and he slept and snored like distant thunder.

From the height of the giant's shoulder, a Pygmy happened to look at the horizon in the distance.

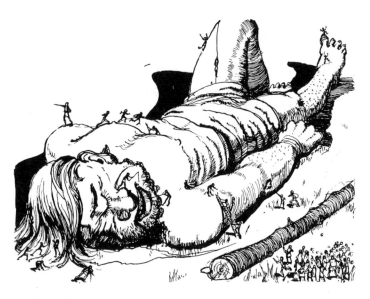

The mighty Antaeus was resting at full length among his little friends

He saw a sight that made him look again and again
—he seemed to see a mountain move! But then he
saw that it was a strange figure in human shape;
not so big as Antaeus, but a very large figure indeed,
and it was coming towards them!

The pygmy ran as fast as possible, up to the
giant's ear that was nearest. He shouted into it
as loud as he could.

'Brother Antaeus! Get up! Another giant is
coming!'

'Nonsense!' said Antaeus, half awake. 'Can't
you see I'm sleepy?'

But the Pygmy looked again. The stranger looked less like a mountain now, and more like a very big man. The sun shone on his golden helmet and his bright armour. He had a sword by his side and a lion's skin over his back. On his right shoulder he carried a club that looked bigger than Antaeus' pine-tree walking stick.

By this time, the whole nation of Pygmies had seen the new wonder. A million of them shouted all together, which made a louder squeak than usual.

' Get up, Antaeus! Quickly, you lazy one! Here comes another giant to fight you!'

' Nonsense, nonsense!' growled the sleepy Antaeus. ' I'll finish my sleep, whoever it is.'

The stranger came nearer. Now the Pygmies could see that he wasn't as tall as Antaeus, but his shoulders were broader. And what a pair of shoulders they must have been, indeed, for long ago they had once held up the sky!

The Pygmies shouted again. ' Get up—get up, Antaeus!' they cried. ' We think this strange giant may be stronger than you—his shoulders are broader! Get up, lazy bones!'

Antaeus sat up and yawned, turning his head this way and that.

As soon as he saw the stranger, he jumped to his feet and strode a mile or two to meet him.

' Who are you?' thundered Antaeus. ' What do

you want here?' He swung the pine-tree so that it made a noise like a gale of wind.

There was one strange thing about Antaeus that I have not yet told you. I thought you might not believe so many wonders if I told you too much at once. The truth is, that whenever Antaeus touched the ground he grew stronger than he was before. The Earth was his mother, as you know, and as she was very fond of him she kept him strong in this way.

Think of it! When Antaeus took a walk of ten miles (covering a hundred yards in every stride) how much stronger he was at the end of it than when he started! And if he lay down on the ground to rest, he got up with ten times the strength he had when he lay down!

Any other man would have been frightened by Antaeus, as he thundered along and swung his pine-tree, but the stranger did not seem to mind at all. He seemed to measure Antaeus with his eye, as if he had seen many other giants before.

'Who are you, I say?' roared Antaeus again. 'What is your name, and how dare you come here into my country?'

'You are a very rude giant,' said the stranger, quietly. 'I shall have to teach you manners before I go. My name is Hercules. I have come here because it is my quickest way to the garden of the Hesperides. I am going there to get three golden apples for my king.'

'You shall go no further!' thundered Antaeus. He had heard of the strength of Hercules, and he hated him because of it. 'And I won't let you go back, either!'

'How will you stop me from going where I please?' said Hercules.

'By hitting you with this pine-tree,' shouted Antaeus, scowling so much that he made himself very ugly indeed. 'I am fifty times stronger than you! And now, when I stamp my foot upon the ground, I am five hundred times stronger! I will make you my slave, and you shall serve my brothers the Pygmies, too. You can throw down your club and your sword. As for the lion's skin, I will have a pair of gloves made of it.'

'Come and take it off my shoulders, then!' answered Hercules.

Antaeus strode towards the stranger, ten times stronger at every step. He tried to hit him with the pine-tree, but Hercules stopped the blow with his club; then he hit Antaeus so hard on the head that the giant fell down.

The little Pygmies were shocked at this, as they had never dreamed that anyone could be as strong as Antaeus.

But the giant was up again at once, ten times as strong as before, and he aimed another blow at Hercules. This time he missed, and the pine-tree went so deep into the ground that Hercules hit him hard across the shoulders before he could get it out again. Antaeus roared with anger, so loud that the sound echoed all the way to the African desert.

As for the Pygmies, they were frightened by the danger of getting in the way. They were even more terrified when they saw their chief city falling down with the shaking of the earth, caused by this terrible fight. They sent up a shriek[1] from their three million little throats, which seemed (to them) ten times louder than the giant's roar.

Meanwhile, Antaeus had pulled his pine-tree out of the earth and was ready to run at Hercules again.

' This time I shall not miss!' he cried.

But again Hercules caught the blow on his club, and the giant's pine-tree broke into a thousand pieces, doing more damage among the Pygmies than I like to think about. Before Antaeus could move away, Hercules hit him hard with his club and sent him head over heels.

Antaeus got up again, his one eye like a circle of flame with rage. He raised his two fists over his head and jumped up and down, as if he would not only kill Hercules but smash the whole world to pieces.

' Come on!' he thundered. ' Let me hit you only once, and you'll never have a headache again!'

Hercules was beginning to see that he would never win this fight by knocking Antaeus down,

---

1. *shriek:* (Pron: *Shreek*) loud cry of fright.

for the giant rose again ever stronger. So Hercules threw down his club and stood ready to wrestle.

'Here I am!' he cried. 'As I've broken your pine-tree we will try a wrestling match.'

Antaeus was rather proud of his skill in wrestling. He shouted, 'Come on, then, villain! I'll fling you so far that you'll never get up again!'

He rushed at Hercules, hopping towards him in a towering rage, and getting stronger every time he touched the ground.

But Hercules was wiser than Antaeus, and he had thought of a way to conquer him. Watching for a chance when the giant rushed at him, Hercules caught him round the middle and lifted him high in the air.

Imagine it! What a sight it must have been— to see the huge giant up in the air over Hercules' head, kicking his legs and twisting his big body helplessly!

And, as Hercules had guessed, as soon as Antaeus was off the ground he began to lose his strength. He grew weaker and weaker; his kicking slowly stopped and his voice lost its thunder. The truth was, that unless Antaeus touched his Mother Earth once in five minutes the very breath of life began to leave him. Hercules guessed this secret; and it might be a good thing for us to remember it, in case we should ever have to fight a giant like

65

Antaeus. But I feel a little sorry for him, even though he was so rude to a stranger.

When Hercules felt that the strength and breath had gone out of Antaeus, he threw the giant's body a mile off, where it lay still. It was too late for Mother Earth to help him now, and his giant bones are probably lying there to this day.

What a cry went up from the Pygmy people, when they saw what had happened! But Hercules took no notice of the tiny sound, thinking it was the crying of some birds that had been disturbed by the noise. He had come a long way, and he was also tired after the fight, so he lay down on his lion's skin and went to sleep.

As soon as the Pygmies saw this, they called themselves together, until they were a huge crowd at least twenty-seven feet square. Then one of their famous speakers got up and spoke to them.

'Little mighty men!' he said. 'We have all seen the terrible thing that has happened. Our brother Antaeus is dead—killed by a man who did not fight fair. And now this wicked victor has dared to go to sleep as if nothing had happened!

'Antaeus was our brother, born of the same Mother Earth. He has lived with us in peace for as long as we can remember. Many a time he has sheltered us from the sun and let our children play in his hair. He never stepped on us carelessly or hurt us. Can we let his death go unavenged?[2] Shall we not punish this stranger? Should not his bones lie beside those of our dead brother Antaeus?'

The Pygmies shouted and clapped their hands. The speaker drew his sword (which was as long as a penknife) and waved it over his head. He cried that he would fight Hercules alone if need be.

After much talk, it was decided that all the Pygmies would attack Hercules and kill him while he slept. Some wanted to send a herald with his trumpet up to the ear of Hercules to challenge him first, but the older Pygmies said that he deserved to be taken by surprise.

So all the fighting men of the Pygmy nation were called together. Twenty thousand archers were then marched in front, with their arrows ready. The same number of soldiers were ordered to climb up Hercules, with bundles of hay and straw, to plug his nose and mouth, so that he could not breathe. But this was no good, for the sleeper's breath blew away the Pygmies as soon as they came near him!

After holding another meeting, the leaders of the army ordered their men to collect sticks, dry grass, and anything that would burn well, and make a big heap of it all round the head of Hercules. They soon had a pile as high as his face. Meanwhile the archers were told to shoot at Hercules at once if he moved.

When everything was ready, the pile was lit and

2. *unavenged*: unpunished.

it burst into flame. Though a Pygmy is so small, he can set the world on fire just as easily as a giant can; and this was quite a good way of dealing with their enemy, if they could keep him quiet and still.

But when Hercules felt the heat of the fire he sat up at once.

'What's all this?' he cried, looking round him as if he expected to see another giant.

Then the twenty thousand archers all shot at Hercules, straight at his face. But only a few of the arrows went through the skin, as he was as thick-skinned as a hero must always be.

'Villain!' shouted all the Pygmies at once. 'You have killed our brother, Antaeus, the friend of our nation! We declare war on you and are going to kill you!'

This time Hercules heard the little voices. He looked about, but could see nothing. Then, at last, he saw the crowd of tiny Pygmies at his feet. He stooped down and picked up the nearest one between his finger and thumb, and set him on the palm of his left hand. It happened to be the same little Pygmy who had made the speech.

'What on earth are you, little fellow?' asked Hercules, amazed.

'I am your enemy,' answered the brave Pygmy, in his biggest squeak. 'You have killed the giant Antaeus, our brother. We are determined to kill you. I will challenge you to a fight myself, alone!'

He picked up the nearest one and set him on the palm of his left hand

Hercules heard these big words and warlike threats in amazement. Then, he was so delighted by the little fierce Pygmy that he began to laugh. He almost dropped the tiny warrior as he laughed so much.

' Well!' cried Hercules. ' I've seen many wonders in my day—I've seen creatures with nine heads, six-legged men, three-headed dogs, giants with ovens in their stomachs and many other wonderful things, but here on my hand stands the biggest wonder of them all! Your body is about the size of an ordinary man's finger. Tell me—how big is your soul?'

' As big as your own!' said the Pygmy.

Hercules was touched by the courage of this little

creature, and he felt a brotherhood with him that one hero feels for another. He knelt down before the nation of Pygmies, putting their speaker carefully down.

'My little people,' he said, 'I would not hurt such brave men as you for all the world! Your hearts seem to be so big that I wonder your small bodies can contain them! Forgive me for what I have done. I leave you in peace. In six steps I shall be out of your kingdom. I shall walk carefully, in case I tread upon fifty of you without knowing it. Farewell!'

Hercules took up his club and prepared to go, still laughing and shaking his head at this new wonder in the world. 'Ha, ha, ha! Ho, ho, ho!' laughed Hercules. 'For once, I am beaten!'

Some people say that Hercules gathered up the whole race of Pygmies in his lion's skin and took them back to Greece for the king's children to play with, but that was not so. He left them all there, in their own kingdom, and their children's children must be there to this day.

They build their little houses, plough their little fields, spank their little children, and do their little business, whatever it may be. And they read their little books, too, of course. In their histories of the old days it will surely still be read, how the brave Pygmies avenged the death of the giant Antaeus by scaring away the mighty Hercules.

6. THE PALACE OF CIRCE

KING Ulysses was one of the heroes at the time of the siege of Troy. After that battle he spent ten long adventurous years in trying to get back to his own country of Ithaca. Many of his ships had been wrecked in a storm and many of his sailors had been lost.

It was after some of these adventures and dangers on sea and land that Ulysses' ship came at last to a quiet harbour on the coast of an unknown island. King Ulysses sent some of his men to search for food and shelter on the island, but they disappeared into the green woods and did not come back.

Many anxious days were spent in waiting for the missing sailors and then Ulysses decided that he would go ashore and look for them himself. The men who remained on the ship tried to stop their leader from exploring the unknown island.

' You are our king,' they said. ' We cannot sail back to Ithaca without you. If you go on to the island, you may never come back! We are lost without your wisdom and courage!'

' If I am your king, and as wise as you say, then it is my duty to go and find our companions and help them,' said Ulysses. ' They have fought with us and shared our dangers in the past; I cannot desert them. I will either bring them back with me, or perish!' He took his sword and spear, and set off through the woods near the shore.

Ulysses had covered some distance inland when he met a young man in a cloak, with a winged cap upon his head. He walked so lightly that there might have been wings on his feet, too. He carried a staff on which two serpents were carved, twisting themselves round it.

You will have guessed at once that this was Quicksilver. Ulysses knew him well. He had learnt a good deal of his wisdom from Quicksilver.

'Where are you going in such a hurry, Ulysses?' asked his friend. 'Did you not know that this island is enchanted? It belongs to a wicked enchantress called Circe. Her marble palace is over there, among the trees. By her magic art she changes every man into the beast or fowl that he is most like by nature. Beware of her!'

'A little blue and gold bird has been following me, and it seemed to call to me,' said Ulysses. 'Was he a human once?'

'Yes, he was once a king,' said Quicksilver. 'His name is Picus. He was so proud of his kingly robe and his crown, and his gold chain around his neck, that Circe changed him into a bird.'

'Now I know why the bird's little call was so sad,' Ulysses said.

'If you go near the palace,' Quicksilver said, 'you will see lions and wolves and tigers! They will run out to meet you as you go near. Before Circe changed them by her magic they were fierce and cruel men. They have become the beasts that they resembled!'

'Some of my sailors have not returned, after landing on the island,' Ulysses said, anxiously. 'I have come ashore to look for them. Do you think that they also have been changed?'

'Indeed yes, I know they have,' laughed Quicksilver, mischievously, 'and I am not surprised. They were so greedy when Circe gave them so much good food at her table! They behaved like pigs. She said she had never seen such greedy men! She has changed them into swine.'

'Into swine!' Ulysses wondered how he could return to his ship, with twenty-two pigs instead of his brave sailors. 'But surely I can save them from this?' he asked Quicksilver.

'You will need all your wisdom—and if Circe has her way, you will be changed into a fox, yourself!' replied Quicksilver. 'But, if you will do exactly as I say, you may save them, and yourself.'

While he was speaking, Quicksilver seemed to be looking for something on the ground. Then he picked a little snow-white flower, held it up and smelt it. It seemed to Ulysses that the plant blossomed at the same moment that Quicksilver touched it.

'Take this flower, Ulysses,' his friend said. 'Guard it and treasure it, for you might seek the whole earth and never find another. When you enter the marble palace, keep it in your hand. Smell it often, especially when Circe offers you food or wine. Remember this, and you may escape her magic arts.'

Ulysses thanked his good friend and said farewell. When he turned to ask another question, the path was empty and Quicksilver had gone.

When Ulysses came to the lawn in front of Circe's palace, the lions and tigers and wolves came leaping out to welcome him. But the wise king struck at them with his long spear and sent them back, for he knew they had been cruel men who would tear him to pieces if they had a chance.

On entering the hall, Ulysses saw a beautiful fountain, which gushed up to the ceiling out of a large marble basin. As the sparkling water fell, it took the shape of a man in a long white robe, then a lion, then a wolf. It was a magic sight, but Ulysses did not stay long to look at it.

From an inner room he could hear the sound of a woman singing at the loom, and the noise of a shuttle as it went to and fro. There were the voices of maidens too, laughing together. He threw open the folding doors and went in.

A beautiful woman rose from the loom and ran to meet him with a glad smile. It was Circe.

'Welcome, brave stranger!' she cried. 'We were expecting you.'

The four maidens curtsied to him.

Circe went on, 'Your sailors have been welcome here. They have had all that they required. If you would like to refresh yourself first, you may join them later. See—we have been weaving their figures into our tapestry.'

Circe had a short wand in her hand. She now pointed it at the woven cloth that was on the loom. In beautiful colours, she and her maidens had made a picture as they wove, showing the twenty-two sailors at dinner. Ulysses saw that they each sat on a cushioned throne; and they were greedily eating the food and drinking the wine. The work had not gone any further; the enchantress was too cunning to let Ulysses see the result of her magic powers.

'As for yourself,' Circe continued, 'judging by your dignity and courage, I take you to be a king. Please follow me and you shall be treated in kingly fashion.'

Ulysses followed Circe into a large oval room. It was where his sailors had dined 'not wisely, but too well'. Since he had entered the palace he had held the snow-white flower in his hand, and he smelt it often. Now, as he entered this room, he took several deep breaths of the flower's sweet scent.

Instead of twenty-two thrones, there was now only one, placed in the centre of the room. It was the most magnificent throne that any king has ever sat on, before or since. It was made of pure gold, studded with precious stones. There was a cushion that looked like a soft heap of living roses, and, over-head, the canopy[1] was draped with a golden cloth that seemed to be woven of sunlight.

Circe took Ulysses by the hand and made him sit down upon this dazzling throne. Then she clapped her hands and the chief butler came in.

'Bring the goblet[2] that I keep only for kings to use,' she commanded. 'Fill it with the same delicious wine that my royal brother praised so highly.'

Ulysses held the white flower to his nose while they waited for the butler to return.

---

1. *canopy:*   the covering over a throne or bed.
2. *goblet:*   a large drinking cup without a handle.

' Is it a good and pure wine?' he asked.

' It is the purest wine that ever came from a grape,' Circe said. 'And instead of disguising a man, as some wine does, it brings his true self to light. It shows him how he ought to be.'

The chief butler then brought the royal goblet, filled to the brim with a golden wine that sparkled and shone like sunshine. He loved to see people make beasts of themselves, and he handed the goblet to Ulysses with a bow.

But, though the golden wine sparkled and shone, it was mixed with the most deadly magic that Circe knew. For every drop of the pure grape juice there were two drops of pure mischief! And the danger was this, that the mischief made it taste all the better. The mere smell of the bubbles, winking at the brim, could turn a man's beard into pig's bristles. It could make lion's claws grow out of his fingers, or give him the ears of a fox!

' Drink, my noble guest,' said Circe, with a smile. ' You will find in this wine an end of all your troubles.'

King Ulysses took the goblet with his right hand. With his left, he held the pure white flower to his nose. Then he drew in such a long breath that his lungs were quite filled with the flower's fragrance. He quickly drank all the wine. Then he looked calmly up at Circe.

' You wretch!' she cried. ' How dare you keep

your human shape?'

She struck Ulysses with her wand. 'Take the body of the beast you most resemble! If a pig, go and join your men in the sty. If a lion, wolf or tiger, go and howl with the beasts on the lawn! If a fox, go and steal the farmer's hens! You have drunk my magic wine, and you cannot remain a man any longer!'

But Ulysses had smelt the pure snow-white flower. Instead of becoming a beast, he looked more manly and king-like than before. He stood up and threw the goblet across the room, where it fell against the marble wall. Then, drawing his sword, he seized

He seized Circe by her beautiful hair

Circe by her beautiful hair.

'Wicked Circe!' he cried. 'This sword shall put an end to your enchantments. You shall do no more mischief. You shall not tempt a man again, to make a beast of himself!'

The sword of Ulysses shone so brightly, and his words rang out with such righteous anger, that Circe almost died of fright. The chief butler disappeared, picking up the golden goblet as he went. The enchantress and her maidens fell on their knees, crying for mercy.

'Spare me!' cried Circe. 'Spare me, wise King Ulysses—for now I know who you are! Quicksilver said that only you could conquer me, and he was right. Spare me—and this palace shall be yours!'

The four maidens wept and pleaded with Ulysses; but he would not listen until Circe promised to change his sailors into men once more.

Then Circe led the way out of the back door of her palace. She showed Ulysses all the swine in their sty.

Altogether, fifty pigs were there; and Ulysses could see very little difference between those that had always been swine and their new brothers who had so recently been men. When he came near to the sty, twenty-two enormous pigs left the others and came towards the gate, with a chorus of squeals.

The swine did not seem to know what they wanted, or whether they were more hungry than miserable.

They dug their noses into the mud, looking for something to eat. When one of the maidens threw them some acorns, they fought for them as if they had had no food for a month.

'Change them back into men, Circe, if you can,' said Ulysses. 'It will need greater magic, I think, than it took to make swine of them!'

Circe waved her wand, and she said some magic words. The swine pricked up their ears and lifted their heads.

It was a wonderful thing to see their swinish snouts grow shorter and shorter, (instead of longer and longer, which had happened when they were turned into swine), and their mouths now grew smaller and smaller, until they began to look like those of men again. One after another, the twenty-two pigs stood on their hind-legs and scratched their noses with their fore-legs, and soon their trotters turned back into hands and feet.

At last, Ulysses could recognise his twenty-two sailors again, looking much the same as when they left the ship. But the swinish quality was not quite gone, for it is a very difficult thing to get rid of. When some more acorns were thrown on the ground (for the maiden was fond of mischief) they all went down on their knees again in a moment, gobbling them up! Then they realised what they were doing and stood up again, looking very foolish. It would take a little time to renew their manliness!

'Thank you, Ulysses,' they said. 'You have helped us to be men again, instead of beasts.' But there was a sort of grunt in their voices still, and it remained for quite a long time afterwards.

'I hope you will never find your way back to the sty,' said Ulysses.

Just then, a bird's note was heard, coming from a tree near by. It was the little blue and gold bird that had followed Ulysses. He at once ordered Circe to change it back to its human shape.

King Picus jumped down from the tree, dressed in a long blue robe and yellow stockings; with a gold chain round his neck and a golden crown upon his head. He thanked Ulysses for his help, and then he went back to his own country.

From that day, King Picus was no longer proud of being a king. He became the true servant of his people. He made it his life's ambition to keep them happy and contented for the rest of his reign.

As for the lions, tigers and wolves, Ulysses thought it was best to leave them as they were. They would be a warning to other people who were fierce and cruel.

When he had settled all this, Ulysses sent to his ship to call the rest of his men. After they had arrived, he and all his sailors made themselves comfortable in Circe's enchanted palace. Here they stayed until they were quite rested and refreshed after the dangers and adventures of their voyage.

7. JASON AND THE GOLDEN FLEECE

WHEN Jason was a very little boy, he was brought up by the oddest schoolmaster that you ever heard of. He had the head and shoulders of a man, but his body and legs were those of a beautiful white horse. He was a Centaur. His name was Chiron, and he was a very good schoolmaster, in spite of being different from those we know today.

Chiron taught his pupils a great many useful things. They learnt how to cure diseases, how to use the sword and shield, how to make music, and other useful crafts. By the time Jason was a young man, he was skilful and wise in a great many ways.

At last, the day came when Jason decided to go out into the world and seek his fortune. He had found out that he was a prince, the son of King Aeson. A certain false king, Pelias, had turned King Aeson from his throne many years before, and he had ruled since the true king's death. Jason was determined now to punish this false king and win the throne for himself, for it was rightly his by inheritance. He departed without telling Chiron. He threw a leopard's skin over his shoulders to keep off the rain, took a spear in each hand and set off on his adventures.

Jason wore a handsome pair of sandals that had

belonged to his father. They were beautifully embroidered and tied with strings of gold. People noticed the sandals as he went by, and they wondered what hero this was, who strode along so bravely without looking to the right or the left.

After walking for some miles, Jason came to a wide and swift river that barred his way. The water was rushing along, and it looked too deep and swift to cross. Branches of trees and drowned cattle were carried swiftly along as he watched, and it seemed to Jason that no boat could cross without being dashed to pieces on the rocks.

' Poor lad! Does he not know how to cross this little stream?' said a voice near him. ' Or is he afraid of getting his fine sandals wet? It is a pity that his four-footed schoolmaster is not here, to carry him across on his back!'

Jason looked round in surprise. An old woman stood by his side. She was leaning on a stick, the top of which was carved in the shape of a bird. It was a cuckoo. The old woman looked very old and wrinkled[1], but when Jason looked into her eyes he could not take his own away from their bright gaze. They were brown and large and beautiful like those of an ox. The woman carried a pomegranate in her hand, although the fruit was then out of season. A large peacock stood by her side.

1. *wrinkled:* A wrinkled face is one lined with the marks of old age.

83

An old woman stood by his side

'Where are you going, Jason?' the old woman asked.

Jason was surprised that she knew his name; and yet her beautiful brown eyes seemed to know everything; past, present and future.

'I am going to Iolchos,' he answered. 'I shall make the wicked King Pelias leave my father's throne and let me reign in my rightful place.'

'Then you need not hurry,' said the woman. 'Take me over the river on your back. My peacock and I have as good a reason for getting across as you have!'

' I would gladly help you if I could,' Jason said, ' but the river is very dangerous. If I should fall, we would both be lost. Besides, I do not think I am strong enough to carry you.'

' Then you aren't strong enough to make King Pelias give up the throne, either!' the old woman said. ' If you won't help an old woman, you ought not to be king. What are kings for, except to help those in need? If you don't help me, I shall try to get across by myself.'

Jason felt ashamed. Chiron had taught him that the best use of his strength was to help the weak. He had also learnt that he should treat every young woman as if she were his sister, and every old one like a mother.

He knelt down and asked the old woman to get on his back. ' I will do my best to carry you over,' he said.

' Have no fear, we shall get across safely,' she said, as she got on his back and put her arms round his neck. The peacock flew up and sat on her shoulder.

Jason stepped into the water, a spear in each hand to steady himself. He began to feel his way across the rocky bed of the river, its cold swift water getting deeper and deeper with every step. The river seemed to rage at him, as if it wanted to knock him down.

When they were half way across, a tree was carried towards them, with its branches sticking out

85

like a hundred arms. Luckily it did not touch Jason, but at that moment his foot was caught between two rocks under the water. As he pulled out his foot, one of his father's sandals came off. Jason gave a cry at his loss.

'What is the matter, Jason?' asked the old woman on his back.

'I have lost one of my sandals,' he answered. 'I shall look very foolish at the court of King Pelias now, with one foot bare!'

'Never mind. It is really good fortune for you,' was the reply. 'And now I know that you are truly the young man that the Speaking Oak was talking about.'

There was no time to ask what the old woman meant, for by now Jason was struggling up the further bank of the river. Suddenly he realised that he had never felt so strong in his life, as when the old woman was on his back. He set her carefully down on the grass by the river side.

'You will get a more beautiful pair of sandals later on,' the old woman said, with a kindly look in her beautiful eyes. 'And King Pelias will tremble when he sees that bare foot. There is your path, Jason, and my blessing goes with you. Remember me when you sit on your throne!'

With these words, the old woman hobbled[2] off, giving him a radiant smile as she went. There was

2. *hobble:* walk with a limp.

something strangely graceful and queenly in her movements, and the peacock spread out its magnificent tail as it followed her.

After travelling for some days, Jason came at last to Iolchos. As he entered the city, he heard one person after another say, 'The man with one sandal! He has come at last. What will the king say to him?'

Jason came through the streets to the crowded sea-shore, where the king, Pelias, was sacrificing a black bull on an altar. The ceremony had just started, and the king was about to kill the bull with a knife, when he saw Jason.

'Who are you?' cried Pelias. Then he looked down at Jason's bare foot.

The men standing by said to one another, 'The one-sandalled man has come! The prophecy will come true!'

Many years before, King Pelias had been told that a young man with one sandal would turn him from the throne. He had given strict orders that no one was ever to come near him unless he had proper sandals on both feet. Now, when he saw Jason, the king was secretly afraid, but he gave no sign.

'You are welcome to my kingdom,' he said. 'From your dress I see that you are a stranger to our land. What is your name, and where do you come from?'

'My name is Jason, and I have been studying with Chiron the schoolmaster,' said the young man.

'I am glad to welcome a student of Chiron's,' said the king. 'Tell me, have you learnt much wisdom from him?'

'I do not pretend to be very wise,' Jason said, 'but I will try to answer any question you may ask me.'

The king tried to trap Jason. 'What would you do,' he said, 'if an enemy came to your house, who could ruin you? What would you do if that man was in your power?'

Jason saw the wickedness in the king's eyes. He decided to say what he honestly thought. 'If an enemy was in my power, I would send him into danger,' he said. 'I would send him to find the Golden Fleece!'

Jason had mentioned the most difficult and dangerous of adventures. It meant a long voyage through unknown seas; but, more than that, it was so dangerous that no one had ever returned alive from this search for the Golden Fleece.

'Very well, wise man with one sandal!' cried King Pelias. 'Go—and bring me back the Golden Fleece.'

'I will go,' answered Jason. 'And if I return with the Fleece, I shall take your crown and reign on your throne.'

' You may do so,' the king said, sneering, '—if you return! I will keep it safely for you.'

The first thing that Jason did, then, was to go and find the Talking Oak. This was a wonderful tree that stood in an ancient wood, and it was so old and tall and broad that it spread over an acre of ground.

Jason stood and looked up into the green depths of the Talking Oak. ' What shall I do,' he asked, ' to find and win the Golden Fleece?'

There was a silence. Then, as Jason waited, all the leaves seemed to whisper together, louder and louder, until a great wind spoke in the old tree.

' Go to Argus, the ship-builder. Tell him to build you a galley with fifty oars.'

When Jason got back to the city, he found that a man called Argus did build ships there. No ship of such a size had ever been built there before, but Argus and his men made a new and beautiful galley with fifty oars. When it was quite ready, it was called the *Argo*.

Jason went again to the Talking Oak, to ask what he should do next. This time, there was no whispering among all of the leaves. Only one big branch of the tree spoke to him.

' Cut me off!' said the branch. ' Carve me into a figure-head for your galley.'

In those times—and indeed to this day—a wooden figure was often placed at the prow of a ship. It is this figure-head that leads the way through the water, like a spirit of adventure and progress.

Jason obeyed the voice of the tree. He engaged a skilful carver to make a figure-head out of the thick branch. And, in a strange way, the carver found that his hand was guided by an unseen power. When the work was finished, he saw that he had carved a beautiful woman with a helmet on her head. Her curling hair fell about her shoulders, and on her left arm was a shield, on which was carved the head of Medusa, with snaky hair. The right arm of the figure pointed forward. Jason

The right arm of the figure pointed forward

thought his figure-head looked like the goddess Athene.

When it was placed in the prow of the *Argo*, Jason looked up at the beautiful face of the figure. ' Now I must go again to the Talking Oak,' he said, ' and ask what next I must do.'

' You need not go to the tree now, Jason,' said a voice. ' Ask me, instead.'

The figure-head had spoken! Jason realised his good fortune. He would have the wisdom of the Talking Oak with him, wherever the *Argo* went.

' Tell me, O wonderful image,' said Jason. ' Where shall I find fifty bold youths to row the galley? They must be strong and brave, or we shall never win the Golden Fleece.'

' Call all the young heroes of Greece,' replied the daughter of the Talking Oak. ' They will make a fitting crew for your galley.'

Jason lost no time in sending messengers to every city of Greece. They told all the people that Prince Jason was going in search of the Fleece of Gold, and that he wanted forty-nine of the bravest Greeks to help him. Jason would be the fiftieth.

When this news was heard, young men from all over Greece came to Jason. Some of them had fought with giants and dragons, some had not, but they all answered the call of adventure. Many of them had been educated by Chiron. There was Hercules; and Castor and Pollux, the twin brothers;

and Theseus, who slew the Minotaur; and Orpheus, who could play his harp so sweetly that wild animals danced to his music.

Besides all these heroes, there was one heroine, Atalanta, who had been brought up in the mountains by a bear. She was so light of foot, that she could step from one wave of the sea to the next, without wetting more than the soles of her sandals! She had grown up in a very wild way, and she talked about the rights of women. She loved hunting and war better than cooking and sewing.

Then there were the two sons of the North Wind, who had wings on their shoulders. They could puff out their cheeks and blow a breeze almost as well as their father. There were many other young heroes, each of them skilled in some way, and altogether they made a crew to be proud of.

When the fifty Argonauts were complete (for that is what the crew of the *Argo* called themselves) they sat at the fifty oars, ready to row. But the galley was so long and heavy, that at first they could not get it into deep water! It was only when their figure-head said that Orpheus must first play on his harp, that the fifty heroes found themselves able to row the ship from the shore.

Then, with their proud figure-head riding in the prow, the Argonauts set off in triumph. The galley sped swiftly through the water, to the sound of cheers and good wishes from those on shore.

King Pelias was the only one who did not wish them well. He stood on a cliff and scowled, wishing that he could wreck the galley with the storm of rage that was in his heart.

During the voyage, as they rowed, the Argonauts talked about the Golden Fleece. Most of the heroes had heard of it before, but none of them had ever seen it. A fleece is the name given to the wool of a sheep. The Golden Fleece was that of a ram who saved two children from danger, in the days of old. He carried a little brother and sister on his back, over land and sea, as far as Colchis. The girl, Helle, was drowned, in that part of the sea that used to be the boundary between Europe and Asia. It is called the Hellespont to this day. The boy, Phrixus, stayed on the ram's back and he was brought safely to land.

But the journey had exhausted the strength of the faithful ram. He lay down and died on the golden sand, his work done. In memory of his brave deed, the fleece of the dead ram was changed to pure gold, and it became one of the most beautiful treasures in the whole world. For years it had been kept in a shady grove of trees, guarded by a fierce dragon. It was the envy of many kings and adventurers, none of whom had such a rare and wonderful treasure as the Golden Fleece.

The adventures of the Argonauts on their voyages would fill many books. They slew the six-armed giants for King Cyzicus. They saved the blind king, Phineus, from the great winged Harpies that used to snatch away his food. They risked their lives in many other dangerous adventures.

At last, they met by chance the two sons of Phrixus, the king who had been saved in his youth by the faithful ram. The two princes offered to guide Jason and his Argonauts to Colchis, where the Golden Fleece was kept.

Now, the king of that country was Aeëtes, the brother of Circe. He was fierce and cruel, and he wanted the Golden Fleece for himself.

'Do you know,' he asked Jason, with a cruel light in his eye, 'what you have to do to reach the Golden Fleece?'

'I have heard that a dragon lives beneath the tree on which it hangs,' Jason said, 'and that he can easily swallow a man in a mouthful.'

'That is true,' said the king, with an evil smile. 'But there are other things to be dealt with first. You have to tame my two fiery bulls of brass— the bulls that Vulcan the Blacksmith made for me in his fire. There is a burning furnace in each of their stomachs. They breathe out fire from their mouths and nostrils. No one can go near them without being burnt to a black cinder. What do you think now, brave Jason?'

'I must face any danger,' said Jason, 'if it stands in my way.'

King Aeëtes then continued. 'After taming the bulls, you must yoke them to a plough. Then you must plough the field of Mars and sow dragons' teeth. Then, as Cadmus did, you must deal with the armed men that will grow there. You will find that they are a very big army for fifty men to fight!'

'My master, Chiron, taught me the story of Cadmus, long ago.' Jason said. 'I think I can manage the sons of the dragons' teeth as well as Cadmus did.'

'This young man seems very pleased with himself,' said King Aeëtes, under his breath, 'but wait till my fiery bulls see him!' Then he said, aloud, 'Well, Prince Jason, tomorrow you shall try your skill at the plough.'

While the king had been talking to Jason, a beautiful young woman had been standing behind the throne. She now followed Jason out of the room.

'I am the king's daughter,' she said to him. 'My name is Medea. If you will trust me, I can tell you how to tame the fiery bulls, and sow the dragons' teeth.'

'If you will help me, beautiful princess, I shall be grateful to you for the rest of my life,' Jason answered. 'You seem to be very wise. Have you magic powers?'

'Yes, Prince Jason, I am an enchantress,' said Medea. 'My father's sister, Circe, taught me her

95

arts of magic. I could tell you the name of the old woman with the peacock, whom you carried over the river. I know who it is that speaks to you through the lips of your figure-head. If you are truly brave, I can help you. First, here is a charmed ointment that will prevent you from being burnt by the fiery bulls.'

Medea put a golden box into Jason's hand. Then she told him where to meet her at midnight. ' Only be brave,' she said, ' and the bulls of fire will be tame before the dawn.'

Jason promised Medea that his courage would not fail. Then he went to tell his Argonauts to be ready in case he needed their help.

At midnight, Medea was waiting for Jason. She gave him a basket. It was full of the dragon's teeth that Cadmus had pulled out of the monster's jaws so long ago. Then Medea led the way through the silent streets of the city, until they came to the royal fields, where the two bulls of fire were kept.

' There they are,' Medea said, ' in the far corner of that field. Be careful, for they will move very quickly when they see you.'

' Are you quite sure,' asked Jason, ' that the ointment will save me from being burnt?' He had covered himself with it before he came.

' If you have the smallest doubt,' said the princess, do not go a step further!'

But Jason had come a long way in his search for

the Golden Fleece. His courage did not fail him now. He walked boldly forward, to where he could see a faint and fiery light that seemed to appear and vanish again. It was the breath of the fierce bulls, which became brighter and more fiery as he came nearer and stood under a tree.

Then the flaming breath of the two bulls lit up the field around, and the tree above Jason burst into flames. Suddenly, the two fiery creatures were galloping towards him, and the heat of their breath became intense. But Jason was not burnt at all, thanks to the enchanted ointment.

Waiting for his chance, as the bulls came towards him, Jason caught one of them by the horn and the other by its tail. He held them with all his strength, one with his right hand and the other with his left. The secret was that Jason had broken the spell of their fire and fierceness, by his bold way of facing them.

Ever since then, it has always been the way of brave men in danger, to ' take the bull by the horns '. That is, to throw fear aside and overcome the danger. It was now easy for Jason to yoke the bulls and harness them to the plough. Their breath was no longer of fire; it was as sweet as the breath of cows.

Jason had learnt the use of a plough from his schoolmaster, Chiron. He had finished ploughing the field before the moon was high in the sky.

97

Then he took the dragons' teeth and sowed them over the brown earth in the moonlight.

'Must we wait long for the harvest?' Jason asked Medea, who stood by his side when he had finished.

'Not long,' answered the princess. 'When dragons' teeth have been sown, a crop of armed men always springs up sooner or later.'

The moon was now high in the heavens, and it threw its bright light over the ploughed field. Any farmer would have told Jason that he must wait for days before the green corn would show itself.

But gradually, as he watched, he saw something shining on the brown earth, like drops of dew. Then, he could see that these were the shining heads of spears. Soon, there was the gleam of steel helmets, and then the faces of soldiers, struggling out of the earth. In a few moments, their armour could be seen. There was a sword in every right hand; a shield on every left arm. Wherever a dragon's tooth had been sown, there now stood a man, armed for battle.

There have been many fierce armies in the world from time to time, and none of them were more fierce than these that sprang up in that moonlit field. But these might be excused, because they had no mothers.

The armed men began to shout, 'Show us the enemy! Death or victory! Come on, brave comrades—win, or die!' Then they caught sight of Jason, and they ran towards him, thinking he was the enemy.

'Quickly—save yourself!' cried Medea. 'Throw this stone.'

Jason threw the stone. It hit one man's helmet, then his neighbour's shield, and then it bounced into another's face. Each thought the other had hit him, and at once they all began to fight among themselves. The fight spread among all the soldiers, so speedily that Jason laughed to see so many men fighting over a stone!

But the fight was in deadly earnest. In a very short time, all the soldiers of the dragons' teeth were stretched lifeless on the field—all but one, the strongest of them all. He had strength enough to cry out, 'Victory! We are famous for ever!' and then he, too, fell dead upon the ground.

Princess Medea turned to Jason. 'There will always be foolish men in the world,' she said, 'who will fight and die for no good reason.'

'But it made me sad to see them,' said Jason. 'And I feel that perhaps the Golden Fleece is not worth so many lives.'

'You will think differently in the morning,' Medea said. 'You can now tell the king that you have fulfilled all his commands.'

But King Aeëtes frowned when he heard this. 'You would never have succeeded alone,' he said.

99

' My daughter helped you, with her enchantments. If you had acted fairly, you would have been burnt to a black cinder by now. I forbid you to try any longer to win the Golden Fleece.'

Jason went away in sorrow and in anger. He told Medea what the king had said.

' Yes, Jason, and I can tell you more,' said Medea. ' He means to set fire to your galley, and kill you and all your heroes. You must leave before sunrise tomorrow. But first you shall have the Golden Fleece, if my powers can help you to win it.'

In the darkness of that night, you might have seen Jason and Medea, side by side, creeping quietly through the trees of the grove, where the Golden Fleece was hanging.

' Look!' whispered Medea, at last. ' Do you see it?'

There was a radiance, like the golden glory of the setting sun, shining from one of the trees. Jason moved forward.

' Wait!' she said. ' Have you forgotten what guards the Fleece?' She took out another gold box and held it in her hand.

Just then, an antelope went by, and it ran towards the golden light. There was a frightful hiss. The huge head of a dragon came from behind the tree on which the fleece was hung. In one snap of its jaws it swallowed the antelope. Jason noticed that the dragon's open jaws were nearly as wide

100

as the gateway to the palace. He drew his sword.

' Wait!' Medea whispered again.

The dragon must have heard her, for its black head darted forward forty feet in their direction. With a quick movement, Medea threw the contents of the gold box into the huge open mouth. The dragon rolled over on to its side and lay full length upon the ground, quite still.

' It is a sleeping dose,' said Medea. ' I did not wish to kill him, as dragons are useful creatures from time to time. Now! Take the Golden Fleece! We must be quick.'

Now! Take the Golden Fleece!

Jason took the Golden Fleece and hurried away from the tree. The golden light of his prize seemed to shine on the path before him and give him speed. As he passed through the trees, he saw the old woman he had helped over the river, with her peacock beside her. She clapped her hands for joy and hurried Jason towards the shore, where the *Argo* was waiting. In an hour the sun would rise. There was no time to lose.

Jason's forty-nine heroes were ready at their oars. As he ran towards the galley, he could hear the figure-head calling to him, ' Quickly, Jason! Quickly!'

With one leap he was aboard the *Argo*. At the sight of the glorious light of the Golden Fleece, the Argonauts gave a mighty shout, and they started to row. Orpheus played on his harp, and sang a song of triumph as the galley began to move. Soon the *Argo* was flying swiftly over the water as if it had wings, homeward bound.

QUESTIONS

1. THE GORGON'S HEAD

(*a*) Describe a Gorgon.

(*b*) What were the special things that Perseus needed, before he could attack Medusa? Describe them.

(*c*) In your own words, describe the attack on the Gorgons.

2. THE GOLDEN TOUCH

(*a*) Why did King Midas want the golden touch?

(*b*) Describe what happened at breakfast.

(*c*) If you were rich, what would you do with your money?

3. PANDORA AND THE BOX

(*a*) Why was Pandora so curious?

(*b*) Describe what happened when the box was opened

    1. the first time,

    2. the second time.

4. PEGASUS, THE WINGED HORSE

(*a*) Tell in your own words how Pegasus was caught and tamed.

(*b*) Describe the Chimaera.

(*c*) If you had a winged horse for a day, what would you do?

5. ANTAEUS AND THE PYGMIES

(*a*) Describe how tall Antaeus was, and compare him to a Pygmy.

(*b*) How did Antaeus get stronger? How did he die?

(*c*) Write about the little speaker; before Hercules awoke and after.

6. THE PALACE OF CIRCE

(*a*) Describe the arrival of Ulysses at the palace.

(*b*) If you could be changed into a creature, say which you would like to be, and why.

(*c*) Describe what happened after Ulysses had drunk the wine.

7. JASON AND THE GOLDEN FLEECE

(*a*) Describe the crossing of the river.

(*b*) Write what you know about the forty-nine heroes.

(*c*) Describe (1) the origin of the Golden Fleece,
       (2) the taking of it by Jason.